Jet Scream

Pete Gupty

RISING STARS

SURVIVAL

in association with

NASEN House, 4/5 Amber Business Village, Amber Close, Amington, Tamworth, Staffordshire B77 4RP

Rising Stars UK Ltd.
22 Grafton Street, London W1S 4EX
www.risingstars-uk.com

Published 2009

Cover design: Roger Warham
Cover image: photos.com/Jupiter Images
Text design and typesetting: Roger Warham
Publisher: Gill Budgell
Editorial consultant: Lorraine Petersen

British Library Cataloguing in Publication Data.

A CIP record for this book is available from the British Library.

ISBN: 978-1-84680-602-5

Printed in the UK by CPI Bookmarque, Croydon, CR0 4TD

Chapter 1

Day 1 . . .

The 52 people sitting on the plane knew they were going to die. And they knew it would be soon.

Flames from the engines had spread to the wings. The lights had gone out and the plane was falling out of the sky.

Some people screamed. Some cried. Some put their hands together and prayed.

Fifty of them were right. They died as the plane crashed into the mountain. But just before the plane hit the ground it broke in two. The tail part broke away and went spinning through the air.

For those inside, life suddenly became a game of chance. It all depended on how you fell.

Two people were lucky . . .

★★★★★★★

11 a.m. . . . Smoke drifted across a hillside littered with twisted metal and shattered dreams.

There was no noise. It was deathly still.

Bags, hats, jackets and books lay on the ground. The hillside looked like a huge untidy bedroom. But only two people were sleeping. The rest were dead.

It was 3 p.m. by the time Jane opened her eyes. She was still strapped into her seat and her head was resting on the ground. What she saw sent shivers up and down her spine. She prayed she was dreaming. But a cold wind and the smell of smoke told her this was no dream. This was a living nightmare.

She opened her mouth to let out a long, shrill scream. And when that scream stopped, another one started.

She wanted to be back, sitting in the plane that was taking her on holiday. But as the sun began to go down and the wind got colder, Jane knew there was no going back. What she saw on the mountain was for real. She would have to deal with it.

Jane undid her seat belt and slowly struggled to her feet. Her legs wouldn't hold her up and she fell onto her knees.

She struggled up again, and fell again.

"Please help me. Someone, please help me," she pleaded in a weak voice.

When Ben opened his eyes he couldn't make sense of what he saw. He shut his eyes and opened them again. It didn't help. He was still on the hillside from hell with a smashed plane all around him. Twisted bits of metal lay on the ground. People's bags and belongings were scattered about.

It didn't make sense. This couldn't be happening to him. Then slowly, it began to come back to him. The flames, the cries of panic, the plane falling . . . falling . . . then blackness.

Now what he saw made him sick with fear. A frightening question flashed into his head. "Was he the only one left alive?"

Ben undid his seat belt and got slowly to his feet. After two steps he fell over. He tried to get up but his legs were too weak.

He stayed on the ground feeling helpless and very alone.

"Why me? Why is this happening to me?" he yelled out loud.

Chapter 2

Jane stopped sobbing and looked up. Was that someone shouting? She looked around but couldn't see anyone moving.

Getting up off her knees, she began limping over to where she thought the sounds had come from. It was like walking through a scrap yard. Then she came to a sudden stop.

Just a few steps away was another seat that had broken away from the plane. And lying on his side, still strapped to the seat, was an old man. He had white hair and a faint smile on his face. He looked a lot like her grandad when he had a sleep in the afternoon.

But was he alive? Or was he dead?

Jane went over and took hold of his hand.

Cold, stiff fingers told their own story. She dropped the hand in horror and stepped back.

Seeing her first dead body frightened her. But being the only person left alive terrified her.

Jane walked on, looking for the living. It wasn't long before she needed a rest. She put out a hand to lean against part of the plane's tail but it fell away from her and went crashing to the ground.

Jane stepped back, tripped over a rock and fell. Then she swore loudly.

The rude words and crash of metal got Ben to his feet. He called out as he stumbled along on unwilling legs. Jane could hear his shouting.

"I'm over here. I'm over here," she yelled. Ben soon found her. They had never met, but they flung their arms around each other and clung on.

"Thank God you're alive. I thought everyone was dead," said Ben

"So did I," said Jane. When they stopped hugging, Jane said, "I'm Jane. I was flying out to stay with some friends. It was going to be my first holiday without my mum and dad. I'm 16."

Ben said, "I was flying out to stay with my uncle. He works out there. It was my birthday yesterday, I'm 15. My name's Ben."

"Do you think we're the only two alive?" asked Jane.

"I don't know. I haven't seen anyone but you," said Ben.

Jane said, "I have. I saw an old man back there. He's dead. I know he is. But he's the only one I've seen."

"But there were about 50 people on the plane. They must be here somewhere," said Ben.

The crashed plane made the hillside look like a battlefield. Like all battlefields, there would be the dead and dying.

"What shall we do?" asked Jane. "Shall we go looking to see if anyone else is alive?"

Ben didn't say anything. He knew they should, but the thought of finding dead bodies frightened him.

What if they found people who were badly injured? What could they do to help?

He looked at the sky. The sun had gone down behind the mountain. It was beginning to get dark.

It was also getting much colder. At last, Ben said, "It's getting late. We haven't got time to go looking. We have to start thinking about ourselves. We need a shelter for the night, food to eat and a fire if we can make one."

"So, what if there are people alive out there?" asked Jane.

"They'll have to wait until tomorrow," said Ben.

"But someone could die if we don't help them now," said Jane.

"And *we* could die if we don't help ourselves," said Ben. The words had a chilling truth about them.

"Well, we could at least shout out, in case there's anyone to hear us. If anyone calls back, I say we go looking for them," said Jane.

"OK," agreed Ben.

For two minutes they yelled and shouted,

their voices drifting over an eerie hillside. No calls came back.

"I think it's just the two of us," said Jane.

Ben nodded. They both tried hard not to look frightened, but inside they were shaking with fear. They were also starting to shake from the cold.

"Do you think we can stay alive on this freezing mountain?" asked Jane.

Ben looked at the clothes they had on. Jane was wearing a short dress and jumper. He had on a T-shirt and jeans. They both wore trainers. These clothes had been OK for the plane, but not for spending the night on a freezing mountainside.

"We'll be dead by morning if we can't get more clothes. We also need shelter from this cold wind. It'll be dark very soon," he said.

"OK, let's get started," said Jane as she looked around.

"If we can drag this bit of metal over to those big rocks then maybe we can make some sort of shelter."

It took them ten painful minutes to drag part of the tail over to the rocks and lean it up against them. It wasn't very good but at least it would help to shelter them from the freezing wind.

"OK. Now we need more clothes," said Ben.

"We can get a jacket from that old man back there," said Jane.

Ben looked shocked. "You mean take the jacket off a dead body?" he asked.

"Well, he's not going to need it, is he?" said Jane.

"That's not funny," said Ben.

"I didn't say it was. But we need more clothes and he's got some," said Jane.

"You can't take clothes from a dead body," said Ben.

"You can, if you want to stay alive," said Jane.

"It's not right," said Ben.

"Well, have you got a better plan?" asked Jane.

"Maybe we can find some clothes in one of the bags or suitcases," said Ben.

"Maybe we can. But we haven't got much light left. Let's go back to the old man and see what we can find on the way," said Jane.

"I'm not taking the jacket off that old man," said Ben.

Jane said nothing as the two of them set off across the hillside. The next 15 minutes would be the biggest test of their lives.

If they passed, they lived. If they failed, they died.

Chapter 3

After five minutes of looking, they hadn't found one thing that would help them keep warm on the freezing mountain. They were running out of time and starting to panic.

"We've got to find something soon. It's getting colder and colder," said Ben.

Jane's legs were blue with cold and Ben

couldn't stop shivering.

As they got closer to the body of the old man, Ben saw him for the first time.

"No. We can't do it," said Ben.

"Yes, we can. We have to," said Jane.

"I can't," said Ben. And he turned away. Jane went over and looked down at the old man.

"I'm sorry, but I'll die if I don't have your clothes," she said, softly. She tried taking off his jacket but it wasn't easy. His body was getting stiff as rigor mortis set in.

"Help me, Ben. I can't do it on my own."

"No. Just leave him alone. He's dead," said Ben.

"If we don't get some clothes soon, we'll be dead as well," said Jane. Ben stayed where he was.

Jane asked him again, "Please Ben, I want to live. I want to get through all this and live."

She looked at the old man. "I want to see my mum, dad and grandad again."

Ben still stayed where he was. He just couldn't bring himself to go near the dead body. Jane pulled at the jacket but it wouldn't come off.

This time she yelled at Ben, "Look, if you want to die out here, then OK. But I don't. Now get hold of his arms and help me."

Ben got hold of the old man's stiff arms and helped Jane get the jacket off him. It was the hardest thing he had ever done in his life.

"Now, help me get his trousers off," said Jane.

Ben shook his head. "No way. Not his trousers as well," he said.

Jane grabbed hold of Ben. "Just DO it! Time's running out," she said.

Ben helped her with the trousers and then turned away as soon as he could.

He was upset and angry with himself. He had just robbed a dead body.

Jane put on the clothes. The trousers needed rolling up and the jacket was too big. But they were helping to keep out the cold.

"Thank you," she said to the old man. Then she went over to Ben and thanked him as well.

"That's OK," he said softly. But he couldn't bring himself to look at her in the dead man's clothes.

The lives of these two teenagers had been turned upside down. They were seeing things they had never seen before.

They were doing things they had never expected to do. And this was just the beginning.

Ben led the way across the hillside, still looking for anything that would keep them warm.

"Let's go back this way. Maybe we'll get lucky," he shouted.

He was trying to keep the panic out of his voice but Jane could hear it. With just a T-shirt and trousers on, the cold was beginning to hurt him. All of a sudden he darted off downhill.

"Are you all right? What have you seen?" shouted Jane.

"Come and give me a hand!" yelled Ben.

By the time Jane reached him, he was part way back up the slope, dragging a big bag.

"I almost missed it. I thought it was just another rock," he said. Jane helped him with the bag.

"Come on," said Ben. "Let's get it back to the shelter. It's almost dark."

When they reached the shelter, they pulled everything out of the bag. Ben almost cried with joy.

There were three jumpers, four long-sleeved shirts, two skirts, some T-shirts, a long nightdress, socks and a bath towel.

Now they had a chance of getting through the night.

Chapter 4

What a night it was. They sat in darkness as the freezing wind howled around them.

Time after time, it took hold of their shelter and tried to rip it away from them.

They were hanging onto life by their fingertips. Without the shelter they would freeze to death before morning.

"How long do you think this wind will keep going?" asked Jane.

"All night, I should think," said Ben.

"You must be joking. When do we sleep?" asked Jane.

"We don't," said Ben.

"What do you mean, we don't sleep?" said Jane, her voice getting louder.

Ben said, "This shelter is the only chance we've got. It's going to take the two of us to hold on to it. If one of us falls asleep, it could mean the end for both of us."

"Not even a little bit of sleep?" asked Jane.

"You can die in your sleep if your body gets too cold," said Ben.

"How do you know that?" she said.

"I read it in a book on First Aid," said Ben.

"Have you ever stayed awake all night?" asked Jane.

"No. Have you?" asked Ben.

"No," said Jane.

They stopped talking. But as they sat listening to the howling wind, they were both thinking the same thing: "What if I'm the one who falls asleep?"

At last, Jane reached out in the darkness and took hold of Ben's hand.

"We need a plan, or both of us could end up falling asleep," she said.

"I know. But what do we do?" asked Ben.

"We have to keep talking, and checking up on each other. You start. Tell me about yourself," said Jane.

So they began trying to talk their way through the night. They held onto the shelter at the same time.

When they ran out of things to talk about, they told each other jokes. When the jokes ran out, they sang songs. When they felt cold, they clapped their hands and stamped their feet.

At times it seemed the wind would never stop and the night would never end. As the time ticked slowly by they asked each other the same question: "Are you still awake?"

It was Ben who cracked first, as tiredness crept up on him.

"Yes. I'm still awake. Now for God's sake stop asking," he snapped.

"Come on, tell me another joke," said Jane.

"I don't know any more jokes," he said.

"Tell me some more about yourself," said Jane.

"There isn't any more to tell," he said.

"Let's sing another song," said Jane.

"I'm fed up of singing," he said.

"Come on, Ben. We had a plan. We've got to stick to it," said Jane.

Ben said, "Look. I'm tired of talking, and singing and telling jokes. I just want to have a rest."

"No. If you do that, you'll be asleep in no time," said Jane.

Ben didn't say anything. He was drifting.

"Come on. Talk to me," said Jane.

Ben still didn't say anything. A heavy hand was dragging him down, down, down . . .

His head slumped forward in the darkness. Jane was frightened. Without Ben, how long could she hold on to the shelter? Without the shelter, how long would it be before they both froze to death?

Her fear quickly turned to anger. She grabbed hold of Ben and started slapping and punching him.

"Come on, Ben. You can't go to sleep. We have to stay awake. Come on. Don't give up now!" she yelled.

Ben could hear Jane's voice but it seemed a long way away. He just wanted to be left alone. He wanted sleep and he was almost there.

Jane kept on at him. She shook him, and pushed him, and yelled at him.

"You mustn't go to sleep, Ben. Come on! Fight it!" she shouted.

Not a sound came from Ben. He didn't want to fight it. He wanted to hug it. Then Jane said the words that saved his life.

"Ben, if you go to sleep now, you'll die. Do you hear me? You will die."

Ben seemed to know the words were about him. They got inside his head and he began saying them, softly, "You'll die. You'll die."

It was a long way back, and a struggle to get his eyes open. But he made it.

He could only see darkness but he felt Jane shaking him. He sat up and rubbed his hands over his face.

"Oh, hell. I'm sorry. I think you've just saved my life. I could kiss you," he said.

"Not now, thanks. I haven't got my lip gloss on," said Jane.

The way she said it made them both laugh. It put them in a better mood. But there was still a long way to go. So they went back to singing the same songs, telling the same jokes, and holding on to the shelter. At last, the long night gave way to morning.

"We've done it," said Jane.

"Thanks to you," said Ben. They smiled and hugged.

"We've done it, we've done it, we've done it!"

Chapter 5

Day 2 . . .

With stiff legs and sore backs Jane and Ben struggled out from behind the shelter. It took some moaning and groaning before they could stand up. But they were happy and smiling, and glad to be alive.

The smiling turned to laughing as they looked at each other.

They had dressed in the dark. But now they could see what they looked like. They looked as if they had been to a jumble sale.

Jane was wearing the long nightdress over three shirts, two jumpers and the old man's jacket. Long, baggy trousers tripped her up as she walked.

Ben had three T-shirts under a long-sleeved shirt and jumper. He looked funny with two skirts over his jeans. They both had socks on their hands, and red noses from the cold. They could have been going to a fancy dress party.

They were in a party mood, laughing and shouting as they ran around trying to keep warm.

It was a strange sight, two happy people skipping around on a frozen hillside with a smashed plane all around them.

After a while, Ben stopped jumping around and stood looking at Jane.

"What's the matter?" she asked.

"I was just thinking about your jacket and trousers," said Ben. "I wasn't laughing when we took them off the old man last night. Now I think they look funny on you."

"Maybe that's what we've got to do to stay alive," said Jane.

"What do you mean?" asked Ben.

"Maybe we've got to be willing to change the way we think. This isn't a game with a set of rules. We have to do whatever it takes to stay alive," said Jane.

"So, what are we going to do next?" asked Ben.

"Well, we had a plan for last night. Let's make one for today," said Jane.

"OK," Ben said. "Let's make a list of the things we need. We need food, water, blankets, matches and a better shelter for tonight."

"Do you think we'll need a shelter for tonight? I mean, how long will it be before people come looking for the crashed plane?" asked Jane.

Ben said, "We don't know if the pilot had time to send out a signal before we crashed. If he did then they can pin-point where we came down. If a signal wasn't sent, then they won't know where to start looking.

"We seem to be close to the tops of these mountains so we could be a long way from people. If no one saw the plane come down, it could take days to find us."

Their happy mood had gone. They were going to have to work hard to stay alive. Jane put into words what they had both been thinking.

"But what happens to us if they can't find the crashed plane?" she asked.

They both went cold with fear. Ben reached out and took hold of Jane's hand.

"Then we need two plans. One for staying here waiting to be rescued, and another for getting off these mountains to go looking for help," he said.

"So do we go? Or do we stay?" asked Jane.

"I think we have to stay close to the plane for as long as we can." said Ben. "It's our best chance of being seen. They'll come looking for the plane. We just don't know how long they'll take to find it. Anyway, it could take us days to get down these mountains. We don't even know if there are people down there."

Jane nodded. "OK, let's start picking up what we need," she said.

But it wasn't that easy. They couldn't find anything they needed. No food, no water, no blankets. Nothing.

But they did see three people still strapped into their seats.

"Maybe they are still alive," said Jane.

"Maybe one of them has got a mobile phone," said Ben.

They got a bit closer. Then Ben went white and was sick on the ground.

These three bodies didn't have the sleeping look of the old man. They had a look of fear on their faces. Their bodies were battered and broken. Death looked ugly.

It was Jane who had to go looking for mobiles. She turned her head away as she felt inside their jacket pockets.

But then she found herself looking at a face burnt away by fire.

She rushed away to be sick.

"Are you okay?" asked Ben.

"Yes, thanks. I love looking at dead bodies," she snapped.

Ben looked across at the three crumpled bodies.

"That could have been us," he said.

"But it's not. We're alive. So let's keep it that way," said Jane. They went on across the hillside, trying hard to cling onto life.

As they got to the top of the hill, there was another shock. It was the front part of the plane. It had smashed into another hillside about a mile away.

"That's the biggest part of the plane. It's where most of the dead bodies will be," said Ben.

"It's also where we might get what we need to stay alive. How long do you think it would take us to get there?" asked Jane.

"It's only about a mile away if we could fly. But we have to go all the way down this hillside and back up the next one. It could take us most of the day," said Ben.

"Well, the sooner we start, the sooner we get there. Let's just go for it," said Jane.

Chapter 6

Getting down the rocky hillside was hard work. Their legs were stiff and weak, and they soon had to sit down for a rest.

"How high up the mountain do you think we are?" asked Ben.

"I was just thinking that myself. Maybe we can work it out," said Jane.

"How?" asked Ben.

"Well, we're a lot higher up than the tree-line," said Jane.

"What's that?" asked Ben.

"If you look down there you can see a line of trees. Trees will only grow so far up a mountain, then they stop. A tree-line can be as high as 4000 metres," said Jane.

"So we could be as high as 5000 metres," said Ben.

"We could be. These are very big mountains. That's why it was so cold and windy last night," said Jane.

"How do you know about tree-lines?" asked Ben.

"I read a lot," said Jane.

"Well, if we are at about 5000 metres, the air will be thinner up here. That makes breathing more difficult. Sometimes it can make you feel sick," Ben said.

"Oh, thanks. That's good to know just before we go on a long walk," said Jane.

Ben just smiled at her.

"So how do you know all that?" asked Jane.

"I read as well," said Ben.

They stood up and set off again. Their legs began hurting as the slope got steeper and steeper. But at last they slipped and slid their way to the bottom.

Now they had a long steep climb up to the crashed plane. It wasn't going to be easy. They hadn't had anything to eat or drink for a long time.

There were grunts and groans as they began the steep climb. They took small, slow steps and kept stopping for rests.

"You were right about feeling sick. How much longer is this going to take?" asked Jane.

Ben shrugged his shoulders. "I don't know. We've just got to climb a bit, rest a bit," he said.

"I like the resting bit. I could just sit here and go to sleep," said Jane.

Ben grabbed Jane's hand and pulled her to her feet. "Come on. Let's go. We can't sleep yet," he said.

Every step up the steep hill was getting harder and harder. It seemed to be taking forever. And they were getting hot.

"I've got to have a drink soon. There must be streams around here. We just need a bit of luck to find one," said Ben.

"Maybe we used up all our luck when we didn't die in the crash," said Jane.

They sat for a time, just looking around them. All they could see were mountains, mountains and more mountains. It made them feel very small and alone.

"You know, if this was a film, it would be about now when the planes and helicopters came flying in to rescue us," said Jane.

"But we're not in a film. And the only plane we've got is smashed to bits on this hillside. So let's go and find it," said Ben.

"OK, OK. Chill out, Ben," said Jane.

The next part of the hill was so steep they had to dig their fingers and toes into the slope. Their lungs felt as if they were about to burst in the thin air.

"It's going to take us all day to get up there," gasped Jane, as she flopped onto the ground.

Ben nodded his head but didn't say anything. He'd started to feel sick as well.

After a short rest, Jane dragged Ben to his feet. Up and up they went, heads down and hands pushing on knees. At last their legs gave way and they fell down, gasping for air.

"I can't go on much longer," said Jane.

"We've got to get to the plane. We've got to find something to drink," said Ben.

"It's our only chance. We can last days without food but we won't last long without water."

Jane looked at him. "Full of facts, aren't you?" she snapped.

Ben lay flat out on his back and didn't say a word. Then he rolled over and was sick again!

"Time to go," said Jane.

Ben got up slowly and followed her.

Jane was walking with her head down so she didn't see the body until she was almost on top of it. She screamed and stopped. It was a girl of about the same age as her.

"Oh my God. That could have been me," she said.

Ben went over to Jane and put his arm around her.

"Come on. We can't help her. We've got work to do," he said.

Struggling on past the dead body, they soon reached the crashed plane. What they saw and smelt made them gasp.

The hillside was black and smoke rose up from the ground. But it was the sickly smell that made them want to gag.

"This place gives me the creeps," said Ben.

"I've seen things like this on the TV news but that smell makes it ten times worse," said Jane.

"This place is worse than where we've just come from," said Ben.

"I know," said Jane. "I think it's called jumping from the frying pan into the fire."

Chapter 7

"I need a drink but I don't want to go looking for it," said Ben, looking at the crashed plane.

"I know. I hate to think what we'll find," said Jane.

"So what do we do? Split up, or stick together?" asked Ben.

"I vote we stick together," said Jane.

"OK. Let's start looking for something to drink. I'm dying of thirst," said Ben.

As they set off on their grim task, everything around them seemed broken, twisted or smashed. But they didn't see anything to drink.

They unzipped bags and pulled out all sorts of clothes. They found three packets of sweets and two bars of chocolate. But it was a drink they needed, and they couldn't find one.

Then Jane had some luck. At the bottom of a blue bag was a small bottle of water.

"Yes, yes, yes!" she shouted.

Ben came rushing over, and they stood looking at the bottle.

"You go first, you found it. But take it slowly. Don't gulp it down," said Ben.

Jane gulped it down. Ben grabbed the bottle.

"Hang on, hang on!" he shouted.

"Sorry, your turn," she said.

Ben started to drink slowly but then he too gulped it down.

"I've got to have more of that," he said.

But they didn't find any more. The sun was going down and it was time to find a shelter. They walked back to a big bit of the plane that was jammed hard into the ground.

The wind wouldn't blow this over. There was a gap where they could get inside.

Ben said, "I think this is as good as it's going to get. Let's take all the clothes out of the bags and put them down on the ground to make it a bit softer to sit on."

"Hang on. We can do better than that," said Jane.

"How?" asked Ben.

"We can drag some of the seats over here. They're smashed up but bits are OK," said Jane.

Ben didn't seem too happy.

"You mean the seats by the dead bodies?" he asked.

"I know you don't like the bodies, Ben. But we've got to do it. We've got to keep warmer than last night so we can sleep," Jane said.

Ben nodded but he didn't move.

"Come on. Let's get on with it," said Jane.

They dragged the seats over to their shelter, pushing the last two bits into the opening to keep out the cold wind.

Now they could lie down and keep off the freezing ground. By using the clothes they had found as blankets, they soon drifted into a deep sleep.

Chapter 8

Day 3 . . .

Jane woke up, thinking she was at home in bed. She stretched out a hand in the darkness, feeling for the light.

"Where the hell is it?" she said.

Ben woke up and said, "Are you all right, Jane?"

Then she knew where she was.

"No, I'm not all right. I want to be in my bed at home. I want my mum to bring me a mug of tea. And I want to say hello to Fred," said Jane.

"Who's Fred?" asked Ben.

Jane didn't answer him.

"I said, who is Fred?" he asked, again.

"If you must know, he's my teddy bear," said Jane.

"Your teddy bear?" laughed Ben.

"YES," said Jane, crossly.

"Oh, right," said Ben, smiling to himself.

"I haven't got a mug of tea. But I can give you a sweet," said Ben

He passed one over in the darkness. Jane took it without speaking.

"I wish I knew what time it was," said Ben.

"Well, we haven't got a watch," said Jane.

"Do you think some of the watches are still working on the dead bodies?" asked Ben.

"You are one sick boy," said Jane, slowly.

"Well, we took a jacket and trousers off an old man. Why not a watch?" said Ben.

"The jacket and trousers helped save our lives. What would a watch do for us?" said Jane.

"Tell us the time," said Ben.

"Very funny. But are you going to take one off a dead body?" asked Jane.

Ben didn't say anything.

"Well, are you?" asked Jane, again.

"No," said Ben.

Jane smiled to herself. Then she said, "Time doesn't mean much to us, does it? We get up when it's light and go to bed when it's dark."

They waited. As soon as the sun was up they crept out of their shelter. It was still freezing cold and they walked around stamping their feet and rubbing their hands together.

"Do you think it ever gets above freezing on these mountains?" asked Jane.

"Not for long. It feels even colder with this wind blowing most of the time," said Ben.

"Well, at least we know we can sleep in this shelter without freezing to death," said Jane.

They jogged around to get warm. Then Ben asked, "Shall we do a bit of shopping, today?"

The shopping trip didn't go well. They saw plenty of fire-blackened bodies lying stiff on the ground. And Jane found credit cards, money and smashed mobile phones.

But they found nothing they could make use of. They sat down to eat part of a bar of chocolate.

"I've never eaten in a graveyard before. At least no one here is going to nick the chocolate from us," said Ben.

Jane just looked at him. Then she asked, "Why do you think we're alive when all these people are dead?"

"We were just lucky," said Ben.

"There has to be more to it than that," said Jane.

"You mean, someone let us off the hook, this time," said Ben, looking up at the sky. Jane gave him another look.

Ben said, "I think we just got lucky and we could do with a bit more of that luck right now."

"Maybe it's coming our way," said Jane, pointing at something in the sky.

"Why? What can you see?" asked Ben.

"Dark shapes. A long way off. They seem to be coming this way," said Jane.

Ben jumped to his feet. "They could be rescue planes sent out to look for us. They could be helicopters that can land and take us off this ______ mountain," he said.

The dark shapes kept coming. Jane and Ben began jumping up and down.

"It's got to be! It's got to be!" they shouted.

But it wasn't.

As the dark shapes got closer, they could see they weren't the wings of hope and rescue.

They were the wings of large birds with strong looking beaks.

The birds flew round and round, getting closer to the ground. Then one came swooping down. Its huge wings made a shadow on the ground.

"They've seen the bodies," said Ben. As he spoke, the bird came in to land. It hopped over to one of the bodies. Its open wings looked like Dracula's cape around a victim.

Jane ran over, screaming, "Get off! Get off! Leave them alone."

Yellow, evil eyes looked back at Jane. Then the bird flapped its wings and backed off. Jane picked up some stones and threw them.

"Go on! Clear off!" she yelled.

Just for a second the bird stood looking at her. Then it took off to join the others wheeling around in the sky. A few seconds later, the birds landed again.

"There's no stopping them. They'll take what they want," said Ben.

"And what do they want?" asked Jane, with a look of disgust on her face.

"I don't even want to think about it," said Ben. They turned away from the grim feast.

"Maybe if lots of them came, someone might spot them. Then we might be found," said Jane.

The thought of lots of these birds flying around made them both shudder.

"I still don't see why rescue planes haven't found us," said Jane.

"Maybe our plane was a long way off course when it crashed. They could be looking in the wrong place," said Ben.

They both stood and looked at the hundreds of miles of mountains all around them.

"Come on, let's keep looking for something to drink," said Jane.

The shopping trip went on. Just as the setting sun was bringing another day to an end, their luck changed.

"I've got something!" shouted Jane. Out of a plastic bag she pulled two bottles of water. "They were stuck under this rock," she said.

They jumped up and down with joy and then tried very hard to drink slowly. It was no good. One bottle was soon empty. They took the other one back to the shelter.

"We've got to keep this one safe and drink it drop by drop," said Jane.

They sat in their shelter as the last bit of light faded from the sky. Then they ate some sweets, talked for a little time, and fell asleep.

Chapter 9

Day 4 . . .

Ben woke up, already afraid. He lay very still, listening in the darkness. Then came a noise that chilled his blood. A sniffing sound. Close to his head.

He was too frightened to move. What was it? What could be sniffing around at night so high up on a mountain?

He could think of only one thing. It had to be a big cat, maybe a mountain lion or puma. He just hoped it stayed outside the shelter!

The sniffing went on. All he could do was lie there feeling frightened. He couldn't run, he couldn't shout, he could hardly breathe.

At last the noise went away, but Ben's fear stayed with him until the sun came up. When Jane woke up, she said, "That was good. I think I slept all night."

"I'm pleased for you," said Ben.

"What's the matter with you?" asked Jane.

"Something paid us a visit in the night. And I don't think it was a hedgehog," said Ben.

"What do you think it was?" asked Jane.

"Something big. I think it was after meat," said Ben.

"Well there's plenty of meat out there," said Jane.

"I know. There's more meat out there than in a butcher's shop," said Ben.

"Stop it, Ben. Why do you have to joke about these things?" said Jane.

"I always joke when I'm frightened," said Ben.

"So why did it come sniffing round us when it can feed out there?" asked Jane.

"Maybe it likes fresh meat," said Ben.

"Stop making jokes," said Jane.

"Who's joking?" said Ben.

They sat thinking about that for some time, their hearts pumping, and their mouths feeling drier than ever. Then they took it in turns to peek outside.

At last, Ben said, "Come on. We can't stay in here all day. Let's go."

They were brave words but it took them a long time to step outside.

They had a good look around to see if they were the only living things on the hillside.

The day was spent looking for more things to eat or drink and hoping someone was still looking for them. They drank their water very slowly.

When darkness fell they blocked up the doorway of their shelter as best they could. As well as using the bits of seats, they now used rocks and chunks of metal to make it stronger.

But they still didn't sleep much that night.

Day 5 . . .

They were both awake when the sniffing began. They both heard the sound of something being dragged along the ground. It seemed a long time until morning.

"It's a pity we're not like the big cats," said Ben, as they stepped outside the shelter.

"What do you mean?" asked Jane.

"Well, they just walk up and take all the meat they want. If we had the guts to do that we wouldn't be getting so weak," said Ben.

Jane looked at him.

"Am I hearing you right? Are you saying we should be like cannibals, and eat the flesh of dead people?" she asked.

"It's been done before now," said Ben.

"That's disgusting," said Jane.

"Maybe. But it's been done. And it saved people's lives."

"Well, I couldn't do that. And you don't even like going near the dead bodies," said Jane.

"I know. I know. I was just saying," said Ben.

Then he said, "I know a joke about a cannibal."

"Go on, then," said Jane.

"Did you hear about the cannibal who went on holiday and came back with only one leg?"

"No," said Jane.

"It was a self-catering holiday," said Ben.

Jane smiled at the joke.

"Well I'm not eating my leg or anyone else's leg," she said.

But not finding any food was no joke. They were getting weaker by the day. Just walking over the hillside was getting harder.

Day 6 . . .

Jane and Ben woke up to another misty, cold day. They walked all over the hillside and only found one apple.

The cold seemed to be chilling their bones and they both felt dizzy.

Jane had a sore throat and the skin on Ben's hands had cracked open with the cold.

They were soon back in the shelter, trying to keep warm.

It was the day they ran out of water.

Day 7 . . .

It was late in the afternoon before they dragged themselves out of the shelter.

Ben said, "I still think we're doing the right thing. They'll keep on looking for the plane. They'll want to find the black box. It tells them why the crash happened."

"We haven't found a black box," said Jane.

"I know, but it'll be here somewhere," said Ben.

"But will they find us in time?" asked Jane.

"I hope so. I'm so hungry it hurts. I don't know how long I can fight it," said Ben.

"If only it would rain we could get something to drink," said Jane.

Late in the day, they found a few sweets.

Day 8 . . .
They were so thirsty they began licking the frost off the rocks and scraping it off the metal of the aircraft. Then it began snowing.

They walked around with their mouths open, trying to catch the flakes. But it soon stopped.

The insect bites on Jane's hands and arms were looking nasty. Ben's head hurt all the time. They were alive but they were too weak to think about walking over the mountains.

"How long can we last without food and water?" asked Jane.

"I don't know," said Ben.

"Didn't it tell you in one of your ______ books?" said Jane.

"It's got something to do with how much you want to live. If you give up hope, you won't last long," said Ben.

"Well, I want to live!" shouted Jane. "But why isn't someone out looking for us?"

"They will be," said Ben.

Jane went on, "They've got planes. They've got helicopters. They've got all sorts of clever things. So why the hell haven't we been found? Why have we been left here for so long?"

"I don't know," said Ben.

Jane yelled at him, "Is that all you can say? Well, why don't you get off your backside and do something about it?"

Now it was Ben's turn to get angry.

"I can't do something about it because I don't know what to do. We're too weak to go walking over the mountains now. Our best chance is to wait here. I wasn't born with wings, Jane. I can't bloody well fly out of here and get help!" he shouted.

They were upset, angry and frightened.

They had run out of food and water, and now they were running out of hope. They didn't speak to each other for a long time.

As they lay down to sleep, Ben said, "We'll feel better in the morning."

Chapter 10

Day 9 . . .

They didn't feel better in the morning. All they wanted to do was sleep. There was nothing to get up for.

So they stayed in the shelter for most of the day. When they did go out, they spotted a plane flying very high in the sky.

"I bet that's full of people going on holiday. Just like we were," said Ben.

"I hope they don't end up like us," said Jane.

"I'm going back into the shelter. It's too cold to stay out here," said Ben.

Day 10 . . .
They didn't get up at all.

They kept saying they would, but they didn't. They felt too ill and too tired. As their bodies got weaker, so did their will to live.

They didn't know it, but they were beginning to die.

They began drifting in and out of sleep, and in and out of dreams. Strange dreams. Crazy dreams. Mixed-up dreams.

Jane was trying to catch up with hamburgers that had legs and were running away from her on a beach.

On the same beach was an old man who was asking for his jacket back. Then she was just about to drink from a bottle of water when it turned to sand.

Ben was dreaming of dead bodies rising up out of the ground and turning into plates of fish and chips, which he started to eat. Then he was in a plane with big cats sitting all around him. They were all grinning at him and licking their lips.

Then Jane and Ben seemed to be having the same dream.

Someone was coming towards them. They couldn't see who was speaking but they could hear what was being said.

"We've reached the crash site. There's no one left alive. We're looking for the black box. Over."

Then the same voice said, "Hang on. There seems to be a shelter over there. I'm just taking a look. Over."

The voice seemed very close now.

"______! There are two people in here. They may still be alive. Get the medics and make it fast. Over."

And for Jane and Ben, it was, over!

Their nightmare was at an end. They were quickly lifted out of their shelter, put onto stretchers, and checked over by the medics. Needles and drip feeds were quickly put into their arms. The life-saving fluids began doing their work. Then their limp bodies, like rag dolls were rushed into the waiting helicopter.

Soon, they were in the air for the second time in ten days. The helicopter was taking them 100 miles to the nearest hospital. It was taking them to where they could start living again, after coming so close to dying.

Jane and Ben would never see that hillside again. But it would stay with them, forever.

It would always be the place just the two of them shared.

It was where they had come face to face with death and had worked together to hang onto life.

They held hands as the helicopter came in to land.

"Shall we go to the same place for our holidays, next year?" asked Ben.

"No. I never like going to the same place twice. Anyway, there wasn't a swimming pool and the food was rotten," said Jane.

Look out for other exciting stories in the *Survival* series:

Runaway
The Boss
The Gambling Habit
Stormy Waters
Flirting with Danger
Fireproof
Why Me?
Jet Scream

Why Me?

'The gang saw him run, and gave a cheer. Showing fear was just what they wanted to see. It fed their hunger for power.'

When Wayne starts a new school his life is made hell by a group of bullies.

Will they beat him down, or can he fight back?

Fireproof

"I'll burn this school down one day. You see if I don't."

When Jack's school burns down that night the police come looking for him.

But did he do it?

Stormy Waters

"I'm glad I don't fit in here. I hate rich people like you," yelled Nick.

Nick wants revenge. He takes Tim's boat but the prank soon turns into a nightmare.

How will the nightmare end?

The Gambling Habit

Gambling is the best feeling in the world for Steve. He's lying, stealing and shoplifting from one bet to the next.

What will it take to show him that there is more to life than gambling?

About the author

Have you ever been hunted by the police, chased by a gang, or tried to stay alive after a plane crash?

If you have, then you know the name of the game is survival. If you haven't, why not read about the teenagers in my stories. They find getting into trouble is easy. It's the getting out of trouble that's the hard bit.

I spent three years training to be a teacher and 33 years being one. I always wanted to know how hard it would be to write books for teenagers. Now I know!

Pete Guppy